INSTANT ART
for
BIBLE ACTION MODELS

Compiled and Illustrated
by
Kathryn Atkins

First published in 1994 in Great Britain by
KEVIN MAYHEW LTD
Rattlesden
Bury St Edmunds, Suffolk IP30 0SZ

Catalogue No 1396028
ISBN 0 86209 553 0

Cover by Roy Mitchell
Typesetting by Vicky Allwork-Brown
Printed in Great Britain

Introduction

Bring your telling of the bible stories alive with these action models. This collection of over forty designs will be enjoyed by both the technically-minded child and those who simply love colouring in. *Instant Art for Bible Action Models* is ideal for use in a variety of situations: family services, Sunday schools, mid-week clubs, holiday clubs, in day schools or at home.

• suggestions for use

1. Tell the story in some way, e.g. drama, storytelling, puppets, overhead projector drawing. Use a good picture book version if you are not confident just to tell the story yourself.

2. Work on the model – one should be photocopied onto card for each child. Always encourage the children to colour in the parts of the model where appropriate using felt tip pens *before* assembling it.

• photocopying onto card

Most photocopiers will take a fine grade of card, and photocopying the models straight onto card rather than gluing a paper copy to card achieves a much better and quicker result.

Fine card (size A4) suitable for photocopying should be available in large packs from suppliers of photocopy paper or from printers. The card will probably need to be *hand fed* into the photocopier, but this does not take too long.

NB You may need to place a plain white sheet of paper behind the page you are copying, so that the next page does not show through.

• equipment required

It is a good idea to make up one model yourself at home first – this gives you a knowledge of the steps to follow and the equipment you will need, and gives the children a visual demonstration of the finished model.

Good Scissors An essential, but should have rounded points.

Colouring Pens Cheap packs of felt tip pens are readily available.

Glue Solid stick glue with a twist-up end is best. It is quite expensive, but holds in place well for small tabs etc. and is not too messy. Available from stationers or Early Learning Centre make a good large size.

Paper Fasteners Available from stationers in boxes of 100 (size 15 mm is a good size).

Sharp Point A compass is useful to pierce holes before inserting paper fasteners. NB Piercing holes – ONLY TO BE DONE BY AN ADULT FOR SAFETY.

Shirring Elastic Available from sewing shops. Useful for masks etc.

Stapler Invest in a heavy duty stapler.

Craft Knife ONLY TO BE USED BY AN ADULT – this is useful in some models for cutting slits or small windows. This can be done at home before the children's meeting - just make the appropriate slits in all the A4 sheets before pieces are cut out. Rest on a piece of hardboard.

• copyright

The material in this book is copyright-free provided that it is used for the purpose for which it is intended. The usual copyright restrictions apply to any use for *commercial* purposes.

Contents

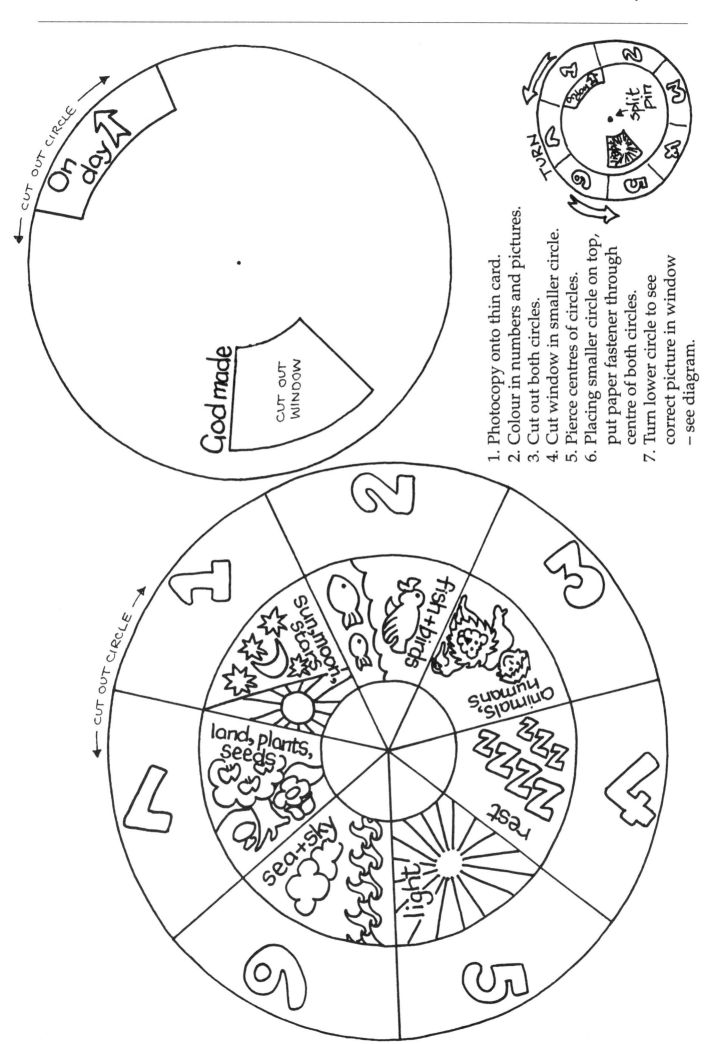

CUT OUT CIRCLE

On day

God made

CUT OUT WINDOW

TURN

split pin

1. Photocopy onto thin card.
2. Colour in numbers and pictures.
3. Cut out both circles.
4. Cut window in smaller circle.
5. Pierce centres of circles.
6. Placing smaller circle on top, put paper fastener through centre of both circles.
7. Turn lower circle to see correct picture in window – see diagram.

CUT OUT CIRCLE

Sun, moon, stars

fish + birds

animals, humans

land, plants, seeds

zzzz zzzz rest

sea + sky

light

1 2 3 4 5 6 7

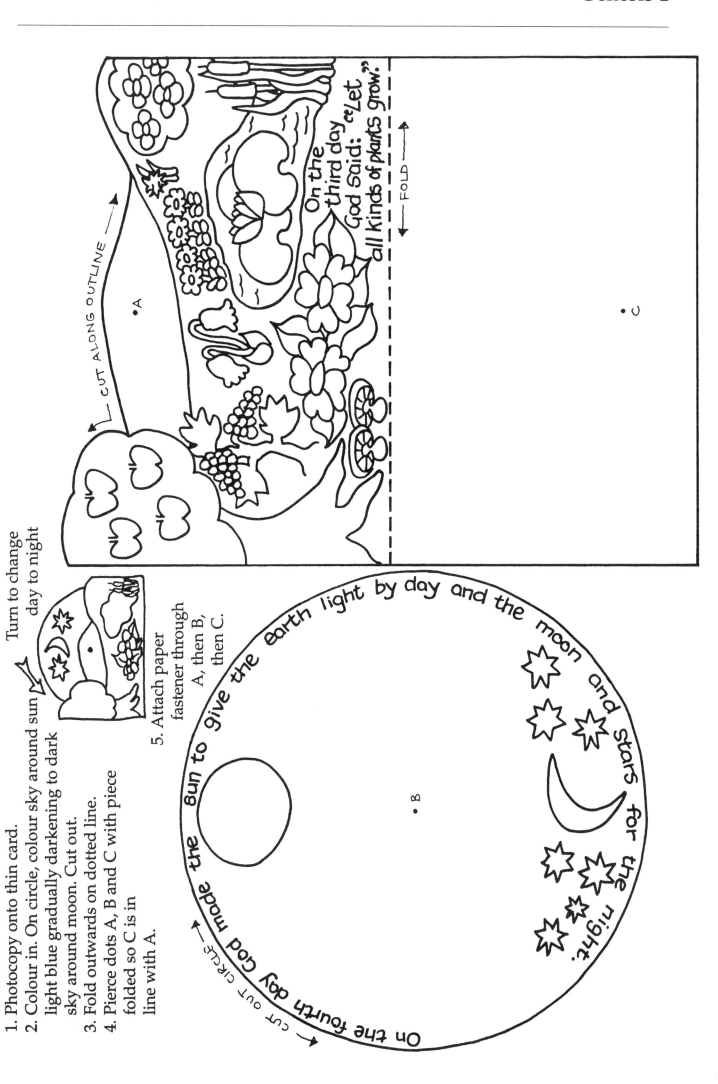

On the third day, God said: "Let all kinds of plants grow."

CUT ALONG OUTLINE

FOLD

Turn to change day to night

1. Photocopy onto thin card.
2. Colour in. On circle, colour sky around sun light blue gradually darkening to dark sky around moon. Cut out.
3. Fold outwards on dotted line.
4. Pierce dots A, B and C with piece folded so C is in line with A.
5. Attach paper fastener through A, then B, then C.

On the fourth day God made the sun to give the earth light by day and the moon and stars for the night.

1. Photocopy onto thin card.
2. Colour in and cut out pieces.
3. Using two sticky fixers or glue, stick a cork between back and front of body – make sure feet are level. (Corks available from winemaking suppliers.)

1. Photocopy onto thin card.
2. Colour and cut out.
3. Glue 'foot' circles together back to back.
4. Pierce dots A, B, C and D – put paper fastener through A, B, C and D.
5. Staple Abraham's head together.

By faith Abraham obeyed God and went

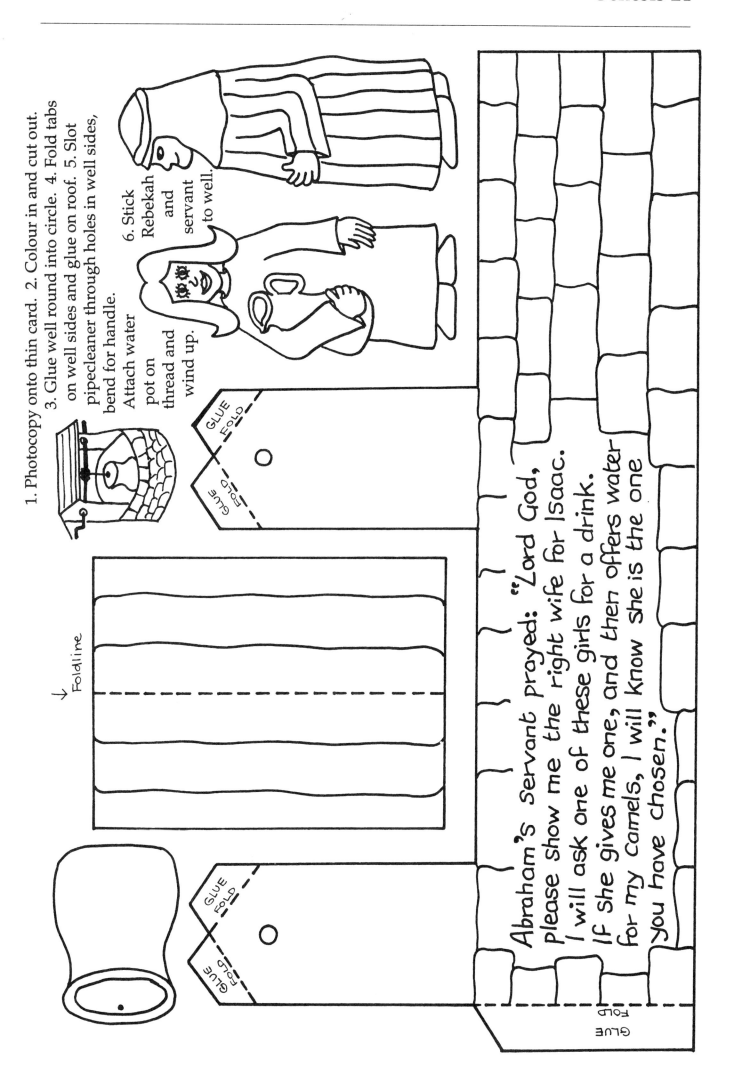

1. Photocopy onto thin card. 2. Colour in and cut out. 3. Glue well round into circle. 4. Fold tabs on well sides and glue on roof. 5. Slot pipecleaner through holes in well sides, bend for handle. Attach water pot on thread and wind up.

6. Stick Rebekah and servant to well.

GLUE FOLD

GLUE FOLD

Foldline

GLUE FOLD

GLUE FOLD

GLUE FOLD

Abraham's servant prayed: "Lord God, please show me the right wife for Isaac. I will ask one of these girls for a drink. If she gives me one, and then offers water for my camels, I will know she is the one You have chosen."

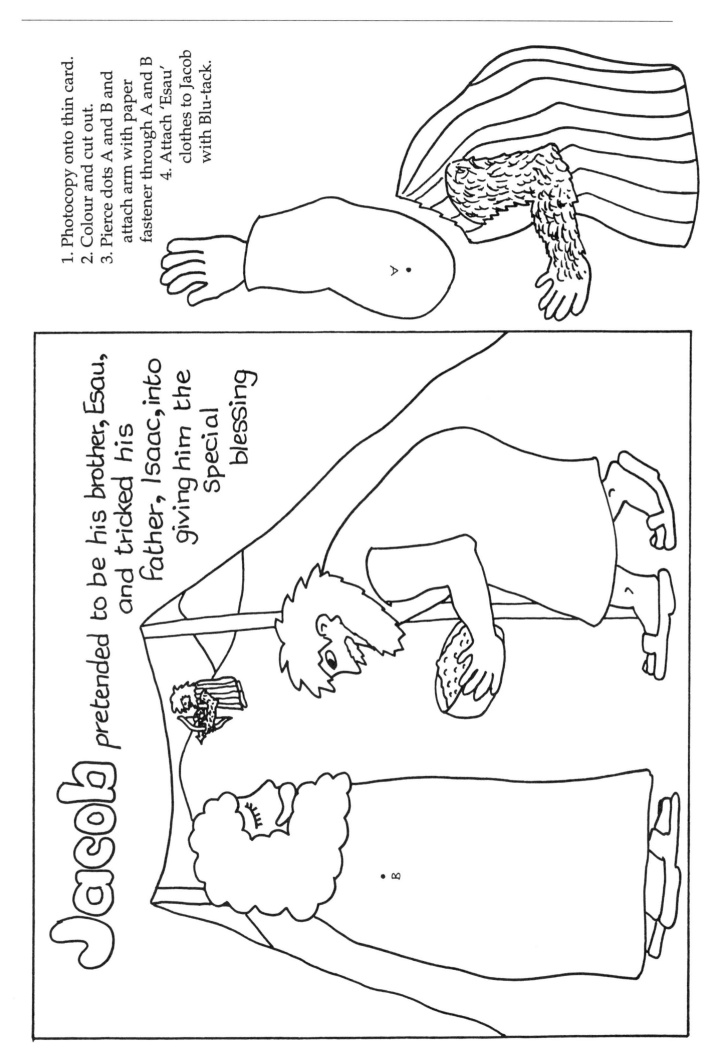

1. Photocopy onto thin card.
2. Colour and cut out.
3. Pierce dots A and B and attach arm with paper fastener through A and B
4. Attach 'Esau' clothes to Jacob with Blu-tack.

Jacob pretended to be his brother, Esau, and tricked his father, Isaac, into giving him the Special blessing

1. Photocopy onto thin card.
2. Colour and cut out. 3. Stick well onto picture – glue **edge** only.
4. Attach Joseph's clothes with Blu-tack – remove them to slot him into well.

GLUE HERE AND STICK WELL IN POSITION

GLUE HERE

GLUE HERE

Who is inside?

Who is inside?

Moses

1. Photocopy onto thin card. 2. Colour and cut out.
3. Fold on dotted lines to hide baby in basket.

FOLD OUT

FOLD OUT

1. Photocopy onto paper.
2. Draw a pattern on the snake.
3. Cut along black line to make spiral snake.
4. Hang up by thread attached to head.

1. Photocopy this and the following page onto thin card.
2. Colour and cut out.
3. Cut out three windows in top circle.
4. Pierce holes A and B then join the two circles with
   paper fastener through A then B.
5. Turn top circle to read off ten plagues.

1. Photocopy onto thin card. 2. Colour and cut out –
   cut off strip with Moses and Egyptians. 3. Cut slits AB
   and CD and slot Moses and Egyptians strip through.
4. Glue waves XY and VW in place, so they open
   for Moses to go through.

PULL

OPEN

X

V

CUT DOWN CENTRE LINE

FOLD

Y

W

A

CUT SLIT HERE

B

Slot Moses and
Egyptians through.
Pull strip to see them
walk through. Open
wave flaps as Moses
goes through, then
close wave flaps to
'drown' Egyptians.

GLUE

WAVES

HERE

C

CUT SLIT HERE

D

GLUE WAVES HERE

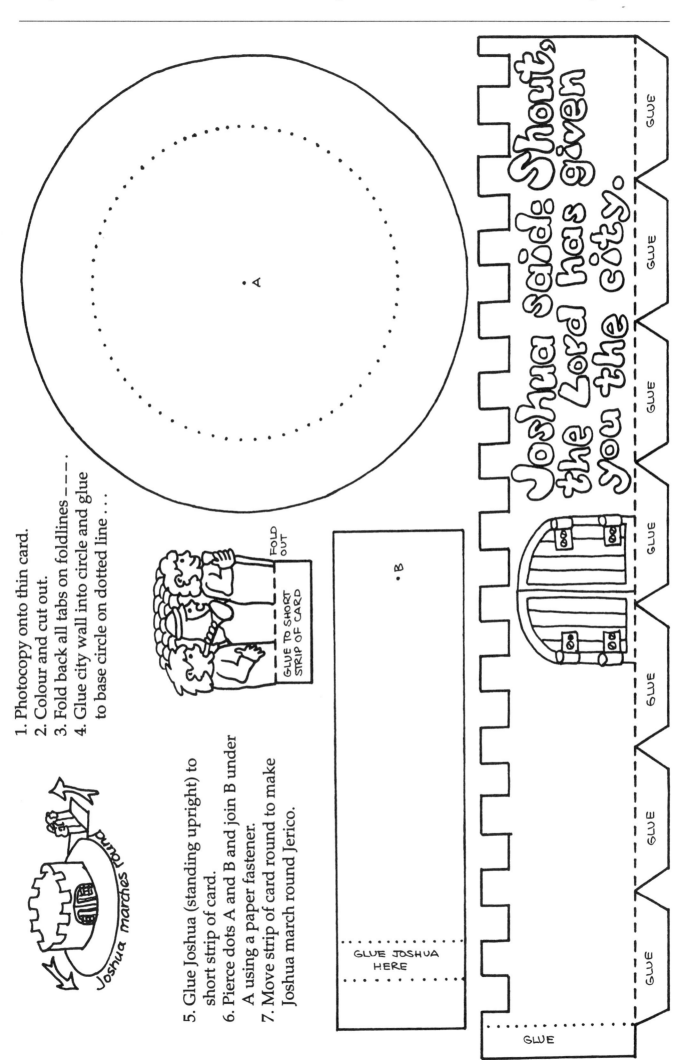

1. Photocopy onto thin card.
2. Colour and cut out.
3. Fold back all tabs on foldlines – – –
4. Glue city wall into circle and glue to base circle on dotted line . . .
5. Glue Joshua (standing upright) to short strip of card.
6. Pierce dots A and B and join B under A using a paper fastener.
7. Move strip of card round to make Joshua march round Jerico.

Joshua marches round

GLUE TO SHORT STRIP OF CARD

FOLD OUT

Joshua said; Shout, the Lord has given you the city.

GLUE

GLUE JOSHUA HERE

GLUE

GLUE

GLUE

Speak, Lord, I am listening

1. Photocopy onto thin card.
2. Colour and cut out.
3. Glue Samuel's sleeping bag together at **edges** only, as marked inside dotted line.
4. Slot Samuel into sleeping bag.

Speak, Lord, I am listening

1. Photocopy onto thin card.
2. Colour and cut out.
3. Cut long slit on thick line on horn (AB).
4. Slot oil AB into slit AB
5. Move oil in and out as if pouring.

Samuel's anointing horn

Samuel anointed Saul

Oil can be moved as if pouring.

A

Samuel anointed **Saul** with oil to show that God had chosen him to be king

CUT SLIT ON THICK LINE

B

B

A

1. Photocopy onto thin card.
2. Colour and cut out.
3. On main picture cut two short slits WX and YZ.
4. Slot long slit with stone through WX from back, then YZ.
5. Pierce dots A and B; attach A over B with paper fastener.
6. Stone comes from sling, then Goliath topples.

PUSH strip to send stone from sling.

Topple Goliath over.

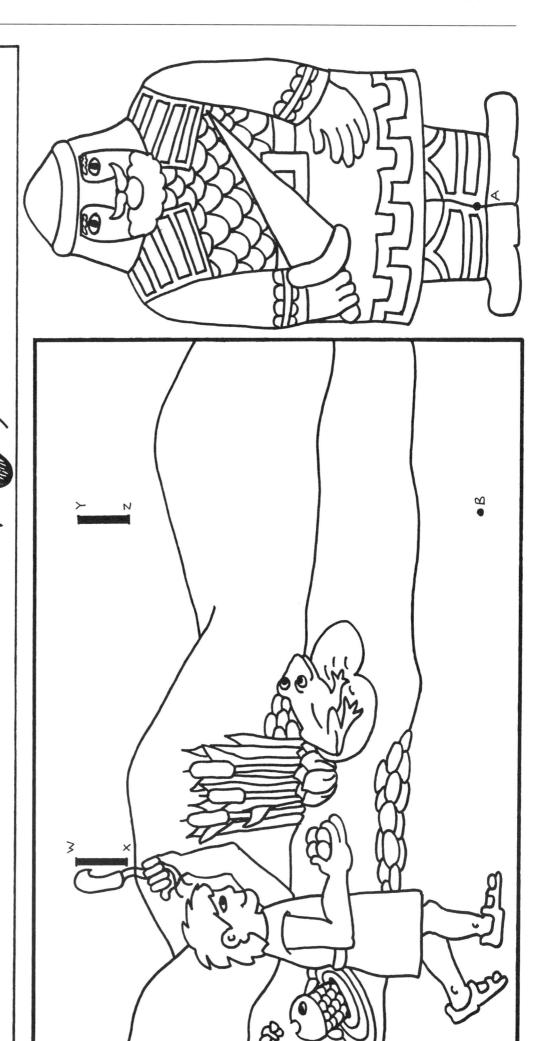

1. Photocopy onto thin card.
2. Colour and cut out.
3. Cut out window in main picture and notch at side.
4. Pierce holes A and B; attach B behind A using a paper fastener.
5. Turn wheel anticlockwise to read story.

CUT OUT

CUT OUT WINDOW

A

TURN WHEEL

B

Elijah told the people to soak the fire with water. Three times they threw jars of water over the altar. Then Elijah prayed to God: "O Lord God, let the people see that you are the one true God." The Lord sent fire down, so hot that it dried up all the water. The people threw themselves on the ground crying: "The Lord is God; the Lord alone is God."

CUT ALONG OUTLINE

SPLOOSH

FOLD

FOLD

GLUE

B

MOVE UP AND DOWN to dip Naaman 7 times!

1. Photocopy onto thin card.
2. Colour in and cut out – cut round outline of water.
3. Fold outwards on dotted lines.
4. Pierce dots A and B and attach B behind A using a paper fastener.
5. Glue large tab as marked and join to back piece of card.
6. Move Naaman in and out of water seven times to be healed.

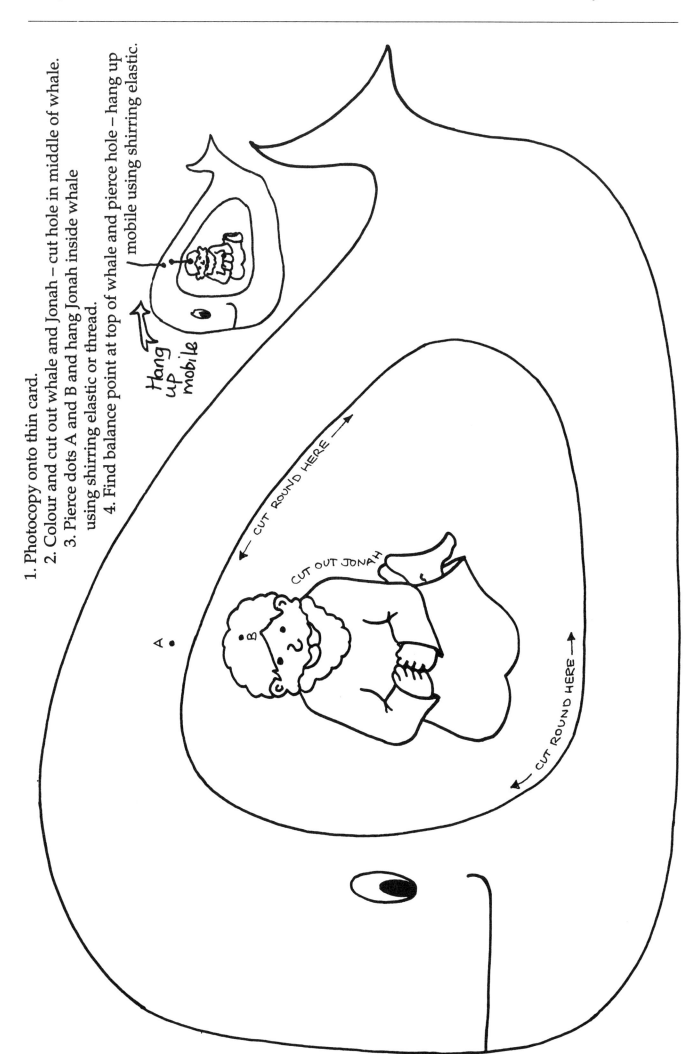

1. Photocopy onto thin card.
2. Colour and cut out whale and Jonah – cut hole in middle of whale.
3. Pierce dots A and B and hang Jonah inside whale using shirring elastic or thread.
4. Find balance point at top of whale and pierce hole – hang up mobile using shirring elastic.

Hang up mobile

CUT ROUND HERE

CUT OUT JONAH

A

B

CUT ROUND HERE

Shadrach, Meshach and Abednego said:

"The God we serve is able to save us from the fiery furnace."

CUT RIGHT ALONG THIS LINE

1. Photocopy onto thin card.
2. Colour in and cut along solid black outer lines.
3. Cut six vertical slits on furnace marked I.
4. Slot strip with picture of three friends, in and out of the six slits, as shown in small diagram.

5. Pull strip through from left to right to see the three friends walk through the fiery furnace.

1. Photocopy onto thin card.
2. Colour and cut out main picture and all plates of food and hand.
3. Cut down solid vertical lines AB and CD.
4. Fold outwards on dotted line marked – – – and inwards on dotted lines marked –..–..– so that the table stands out from wall (scoring lines first helps).
5. Stick food on table and hand on wall.
6. Write words on wall – Mene, mene, tekel, parsin.

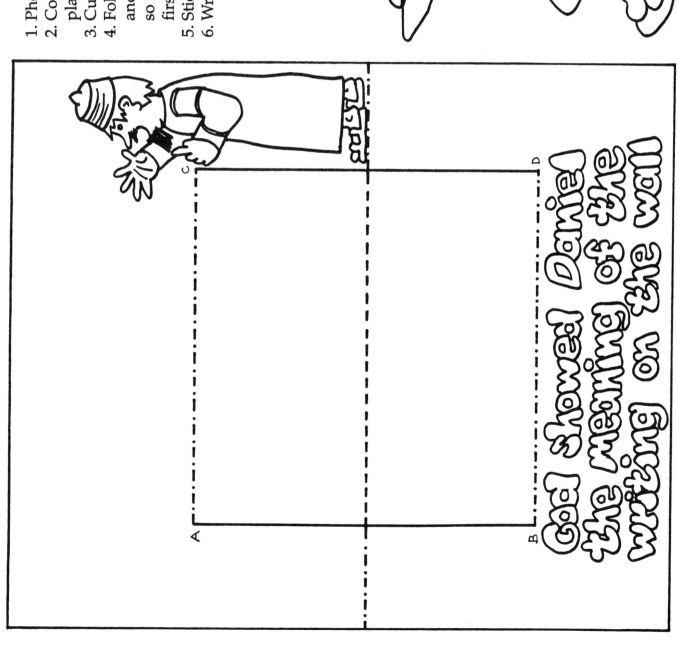

1. Photocopy onto thin card. 2. Colour and cut out lion mask.
3. Cut out eye holes.
4. Pierce at A and B and re-inforce with self-adhesive plastic washers.
5. Tie a length of shirring elastic through these holes
   to go round back of head.

SUGGESTION
You could act out
the story – but
remember that the
lions were not fierce
to Daniel!

1. Photocopy onto thin card.
2. Colour and cut out city wall and people.
3. Write along top of city wall the words 'Everyone knew that the work had been done with God's help'.
4. Glue edge of city wall and stick together in circle.
5. Stick the people praising God around the top inside edge of city wall, facing outwards.

CUT ALONG HERE

GLUE HERE

GLUE HERE

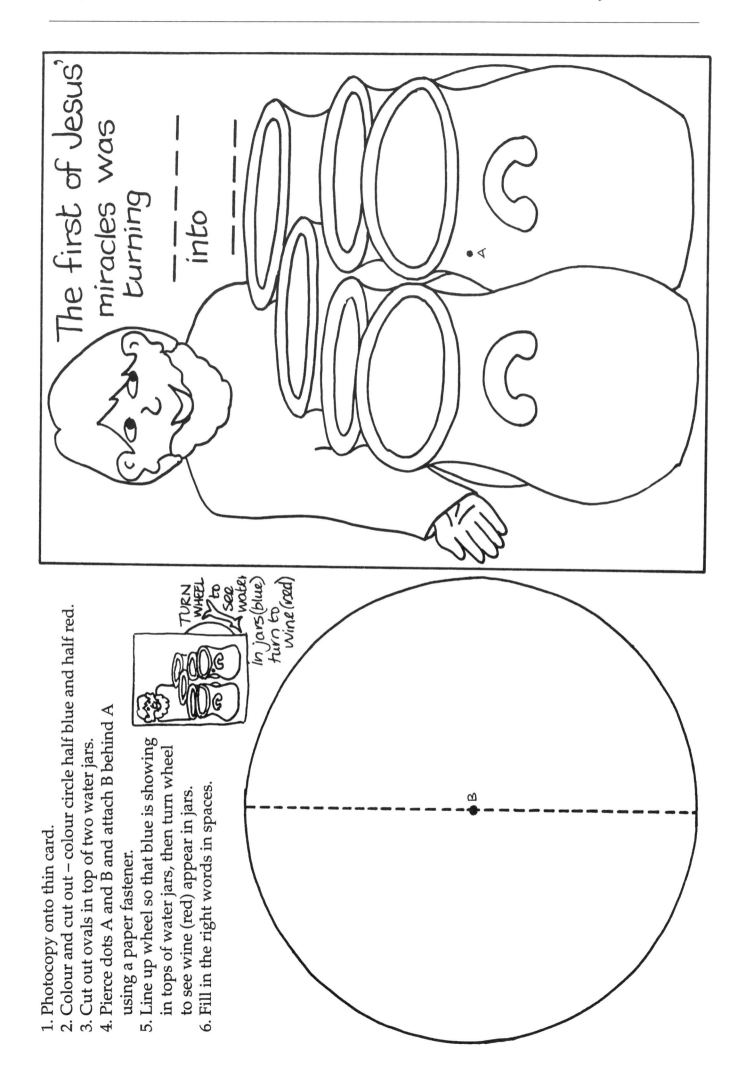

The first of Jesus' miracles was turning _ _ _ _ _ _ _ into _ _ _ _

TURN WHEEL to see water. In jars (blue) turn to wine (red)

1. Photocopy onto thin card.
2. Colour and cut out – colour circle half blue and half red.
3. Cut out ovals in top of two water jars.
4. Pierce dots A and B and attach B behind A using a paper fastener.
5. Line up wheel so that blue is showing in tops of water jars, then turn wheel to see wine (red) appear in jars.
6. Fill in the right words in spaces.

The lame man had faith that Jesus would heal him

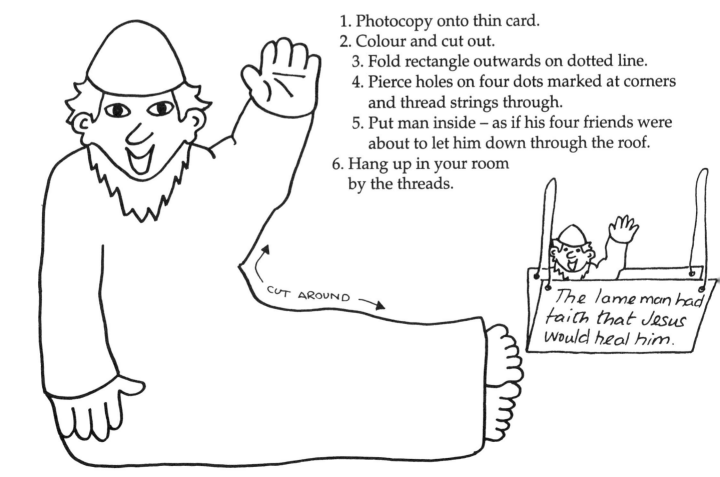

1. Photocopy onto thin card.
2. Colour and cut out.
   3. Fold rectangle outwards on dotted line.
   4. Pierce holes on four dots marked at corners and thread strings through.
   5. Put man inside – as if his four friends were about to let him down through the roof.
6. Hang up in your room by the threads.

CUT AROUND

The lame man had faith that Jesus would heal him.

1. Photocopy onto thin card. 2. Colour and cut out.
3. Cut off long thin strip with dot B marked on it.
4. Fold picture inwards on dotted lines – · – · –.
5. Cut slit XY. 6. Pierce dots A and B and attach with paper fastener through A, then through **slit**, then B.

Pull to move centurion to Jesus and back

The centurion said: " Just say the word, and my servant will be healed."

Go! It will be done just as you believed it would.

And his servant was healed at that very hour.

The woman gave her most precious possession to Jesus

Luke 7:36–50

1. Photocopy onto thin card.
2. Colour and cut out – draw pattern on back.
3. Fold together along dotted line – – –.
4. Write inside the words 'I will give my best to Jesus – time, money, effort'
5. Cut small hole in top of bottle and tie a loop of ribbon through it.

CUT OUT

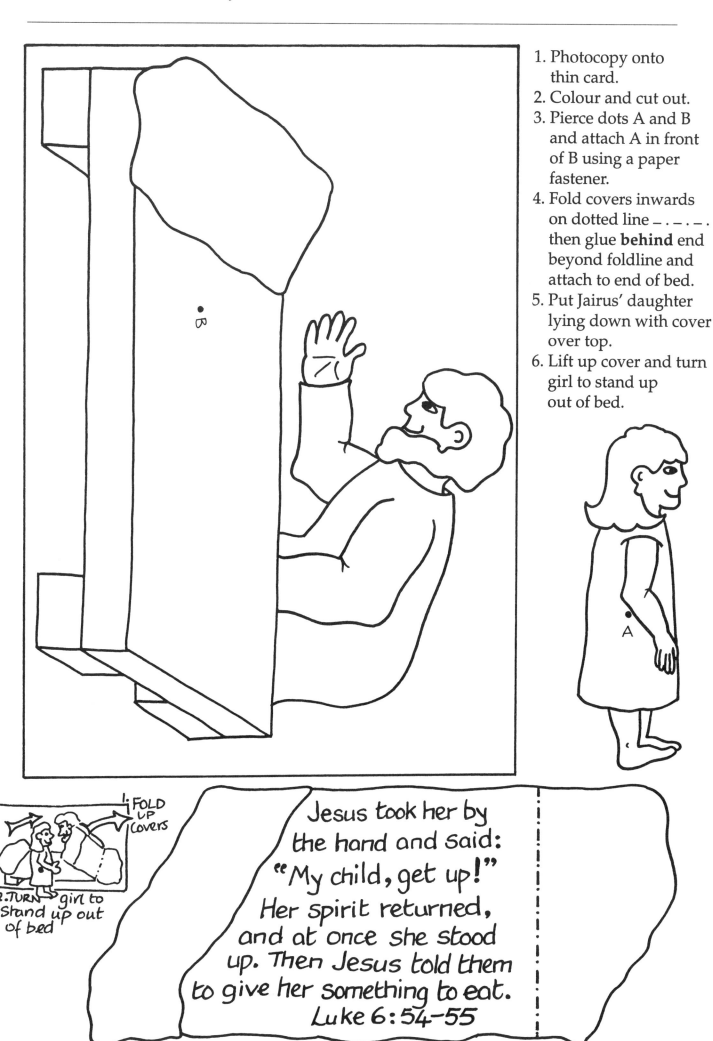

1. Photocopy onto thin card.
2. Colour and cut out.
3. Pierce dots A and B and attach A in front of B using a paper fastener.
4. Fold covers inwards on dotted line _ . _ . _ . then glue **behind** end beyond foldline and attach to end of bed.
5. Put Jairus' daughter lying down with cover over top.
6. Lift up cover and turn girl to stand up out of bed.

1. FOLD UP COVERS

2. TURN girl to stand up out of bed

Jesus took her by the hand and said: "My child, get up!" Her spirit returned, and at once she stood up. Then Jesus told them to give her something to eat.
Luke 6:54-55

1. Photocopy onto thin card.
2. Colour and cut out.
3. Fold outwards on dotted line _ _ _ .

4. Make five loaves and two fishes from brown and blue paper – stick inside.

The little boy gave his 5 loaves and 2 fishes to Jesus. Jesus used them to feed the hungry people.

FOLD

FOLD

Be generous and willing to share
2 Timothy 6:18

The little boy
foldline

fold line

loaves and fishes stuck inside

1. Photocopy onto thin card.
2. Cut out all shapes and colour in.
3. Colour mud patch brown.
4. Cover pool shape with aluminium foil.
5. Cut out finger holes on finger puppets of Jesus and the blind man.
6. Stick blind face onto blind man using sticky putty.
7. Act out the story of the healing of the blind man using your finger puppets – when man is healed, take off the blind face so he can see!

1. Photocopy onto thin card.
2. Colour and cut out.
3. Cut out two windows in main picture.
4. Pierce dots A and B and attach B behind A using a paper fastener.
5. Turn wheel to see ten lepers going away healed to show the priests, then only one leper coming back to Jesus to say 'thank you'.

TURN WHEEL
To see 1 leper coming to say Thankyou.

CUT OUT WINDOW

10 lepers were healed....

CUT OUT WINDOW

...but only one said thank you

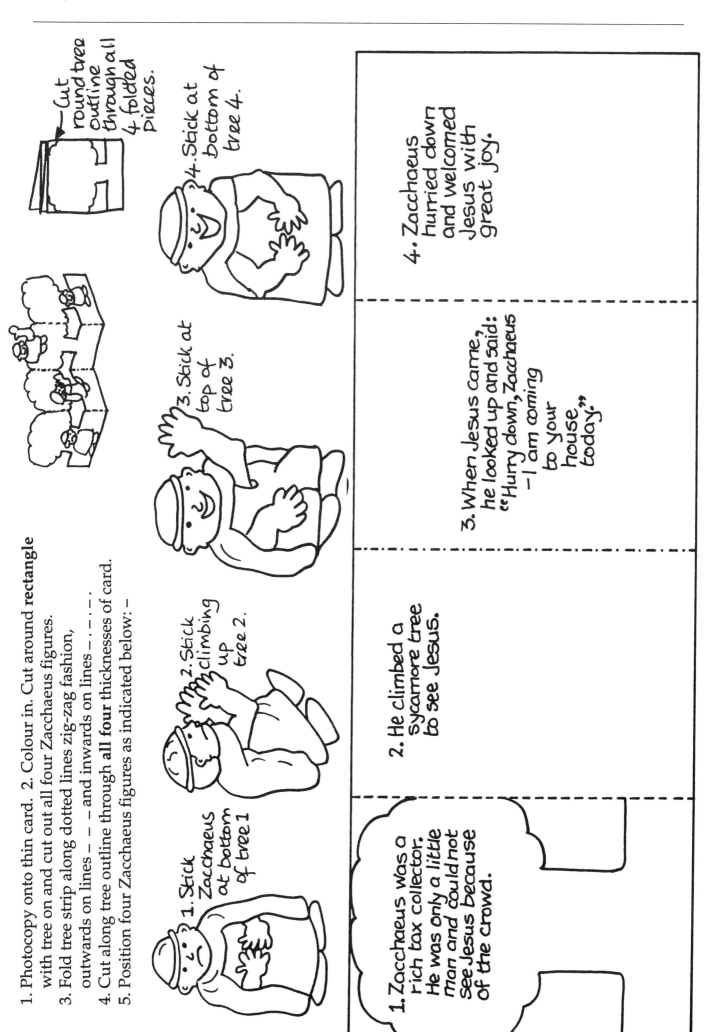

Cut round tree outline through all 4 folded pieces.

1. Photocopy onto thin card. 2. Colour in. Cut around **rectangle** with tree on and cut out all four Zacchaeus figures.
3. Fold tree strip along dotted lines zig-zag fashion, outwards on lines – – – and inwards on lines –..–..–.
4. Cut along tree outline through **all four** thicknesses of card.
5. Position four Zacchaeus figures as indicated below: –

1. Stick Zacchaeus at bottom of tree 1.

2. Stick climbing up tree 2.

3. Stick at top of tree 3.

4. Stick at bottom of tree 4.

1. Zacchaeus was a rich tax collector. He was only a little man and could not see Jesus because of the crowd.

2. He climbed a sycamore tree to see Jesus.

3. When Jesus came, he looked up and said: "Hurry down, Zacchaeus – I am coming to your house today."

4. Zacchaeus hurried down and welcomed Jesus with great joy.

1. Photocopy onto thin card. 2. Cut out.
3. Join back and front of sheep using a cork fastened on
   with Blu-tack or sticky fixers – make sure feet are level
   before sticking. (Corks available from winemaking suppliers.)
4. You could play a 'lost sheep' game –
   everyone goes out of the room
   while one person hides the sheep.
   See who can find the 'lost sheep'.

33 JESUS' PARABLES 2 – THE TWO HOUSES   Matthew 7:24-27

1. Photocopy onto thin card.
2. Colour in and cut out.
3. Sellotape a safety pin onto
   the back to make a badge.

1. Photocopy onto thin card.
2. Colour and cut out.
3. Fold on dotted lines: –
   inwards on lines marked – .. – .. –
   outwards on lines marked – – – .
4. Draw camel face on other side of head.

Zig-zag fold camel so it stands up.

Seek God's Kingdom

1. Photocopy onto thin card (this page).
2. Colour in lettering and cut out.
3. See page two of model for further instructions.

1. Photocopy this page onto **paper** – if possible,
   a contrasting colour to the card on page 1.
2. Join dots of lettering – in rainbow colours if you like!
3. Cut out.
4. Fold 'the precious pearl' card outwards
   and stick paper circle with lettering inside.

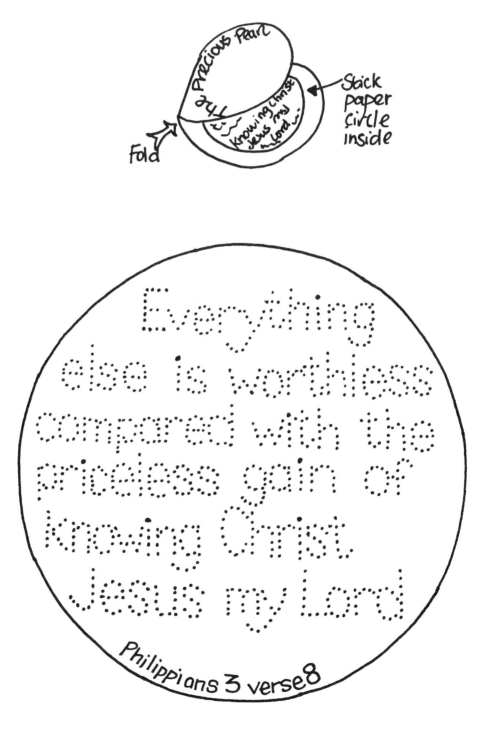

1. Photocopy onto thin card.
2. Colour in and cut round **outer** rectangle – cut out foods.
3. Fold **outwards** on – . . – . . – lines and **inwards** on – – – lines.
4. Through all four thicknesses of card, cut outline of man's head and shoulders.
5. Draw faces on other three people and colour in.
6. Stick foods on table. 7. Reverse the zig-zag folds and stand up.

STICK FOOD HERE.

God calls

God

when

Come

Two men in clothes that gleamed like lightning stood inside the tomb. They said to the women: "Why do you look for the living among the dead? Jesus is not here; he has risen!"

GLUE HERE

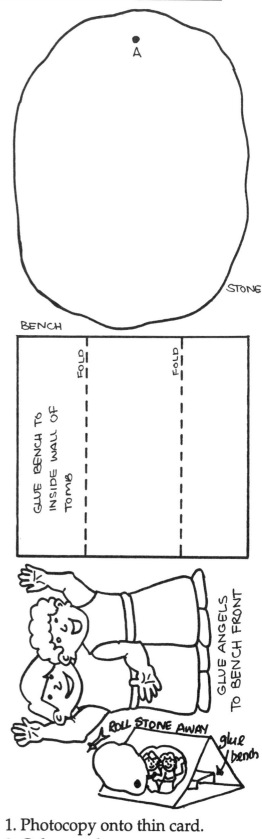

STONE

BENCH

FOLD   FOLD

GLUE BENCH TO INSIDE WALL OF TOMB

GLUE ANGELS TO BENCH FRONT

ROLL STONE AWAY

glue bench

1. Photocopy onto thin card.
2. Colour and cut out.
3. Fold out on all dotted lines.
4. Glue tomb into tent shape.
5. Pierce dots A and B – attach A over B using a paper fastener.
6. Glue folded bench to back inside wall of tomb.
7. Glue angels to front of bench so they can be seen when stone rolled away.

FOLD

Jesus was taken up to heaven as they watched him, and a cloud hid him from their sight.

1. Photocopy onto thin card.
2. Colour and cut out.
3. Fold cloud inwards on dotted line _ . _ . _ .
4. Glue back of cloud **beyond** dotted line **only**.
5. Stick in position marked on main picture.
6. Fold cloud down to see Jesus disappear from their sight.

GLUE CLOUD END HERE

Jesus said to the disciples, "When the Spirit comes upon you, you will be filled with power and you will be witnesses for me".

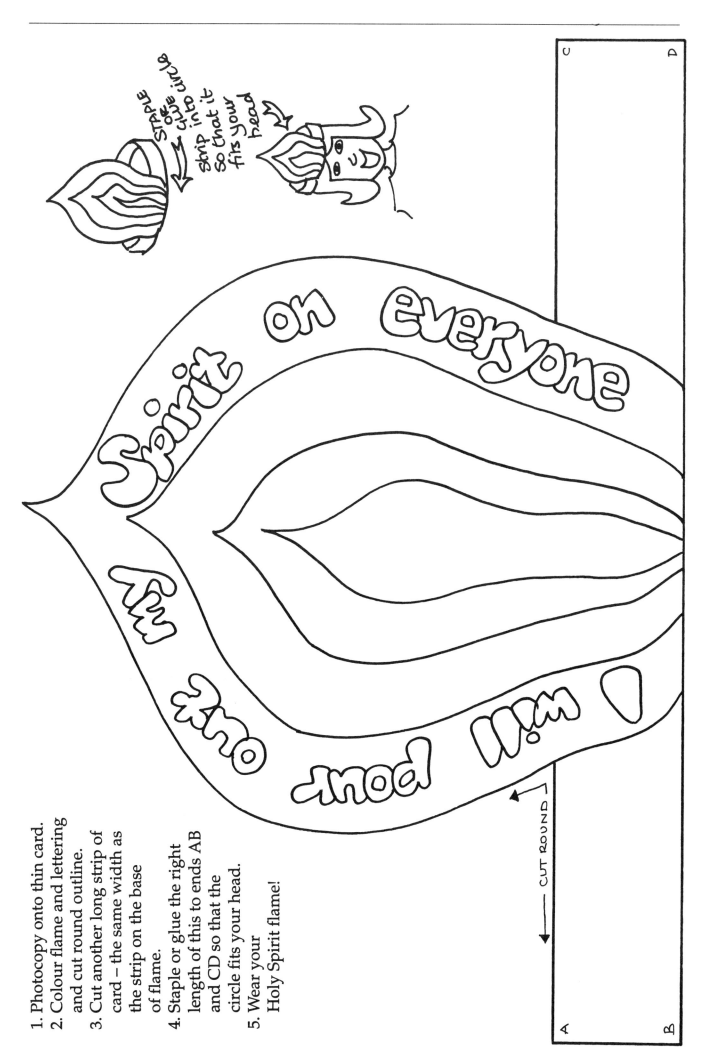

STAPLE OR glue circle
strip into circle
so that it
fits your
head

Spirit on everyone will pour out my

CUT ROUND

1. Photocopy onto thin card.
2. Colour flame and lettering and cut round outline.
3. Cut another long strip of card – the same width as the strip on the base of flame.
4. Staple or glue the right length of this to ends AB and CD so that the circle fits your head.
5. Wear your Holy Spirit flame!

1. Photocopy this page onto thin card and page two onto paper.
2. Colour and cut out.
3. Cut man in half along thick line at middle.
4. Take zig-zag folded strip of paper from page two and glue top to head and bottom to legs of lame man.
5. Hang up lame man by piece of shirring elastic from top of head.

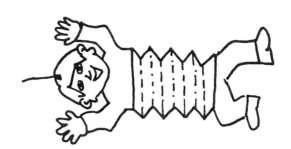

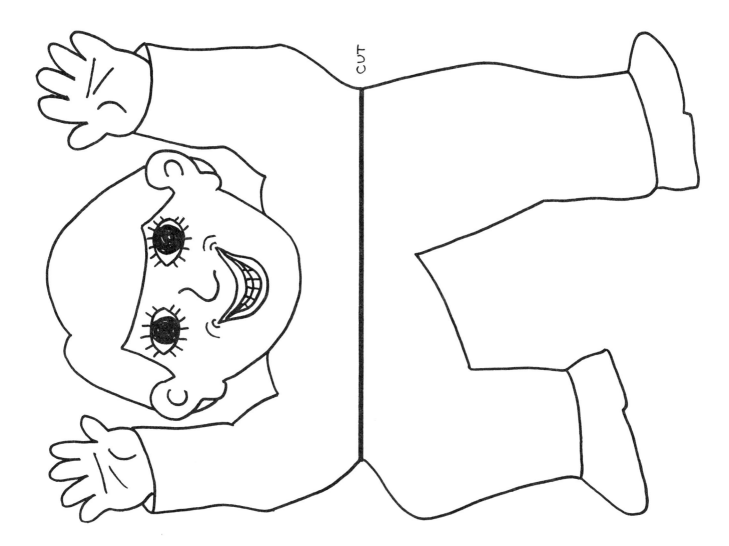

CUT

GLUE TO BODY

Peter said:

"In the name of

Jesus Christ

of Nazareth

I order you to

get up and walk!"

The man went

walking

and jumping

and praising God.

GLUE TO LEGS

1. Photocopy onto **paper**.
2. Cut out.
3. Zig-zag fold the strip, outwards on _ _ _ lines and inwards on _ . _ . _ lines.

The Ethiopian man said:

"Here is some water. What is to keep me from being baptised."

C ⌐ ⌐ D

A ⌐ ⌐ B

1. Photocopy onto thin card.
2. Colour and cut out.
3. Cut slits AB and CD on main picture.
4. Slot long strip into slits from front, so that Ethiopian can ride along to the water in his chariot.

Pull to see Ethiopian ride along to the water.

1. Photocopy onto thin card.
2. Cut out around rectangle and cut off strip with Eutychus, along line XY.
3. Colour in.
4. Pierce dots A and B.
5. Cut along **curved** slits PQ and RS.
6. Slot strip XY from back through RS and PQ, so that Eutychus can be seen on main picture.
7. Attach with a paper fastener through A then B.
8. Move strip to see Eutychus fall out of window.

Eutychus went to sleep while Paul was talking and fell out of the window (Acts 20:7-12)

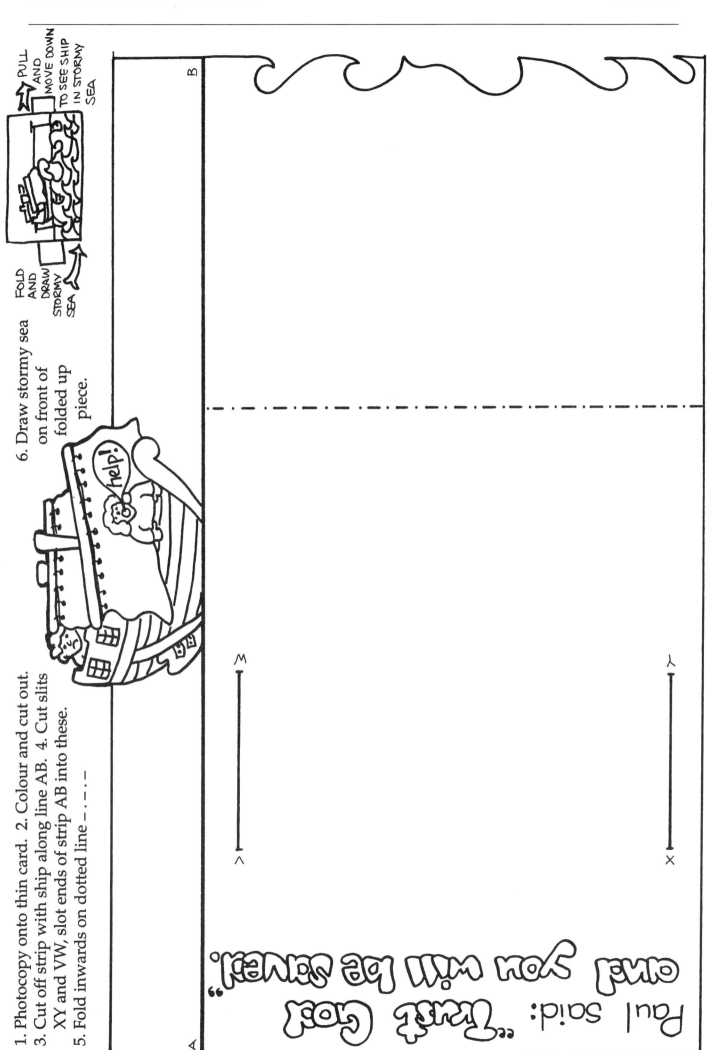

1. Photocopy onto thin card. 2. Colour and cut out.
3. Cut off strip with ship along line AB. 4. Cut slits XY and VW, slot ends of strip AB into these.
5. Fold inwards on dotted line _ . _ . _

6. Draw stormy sea on front of folded up piece.

FOLD AND DRAW STORMY SEA

PULL AND MOVE DOWN TO SEE SHIP IN STORMY SEA

help!

Paul said: "Trust God and you will be saved!"